# AFTERLIFE

## A Company You Can Be

The afterlife is under new management...

As CEO of a thoroughly modernised afterlife, Jack Fortune has faced more than his fair share of challenges, triumphing time and time again. Troubled markets. Political opposition. The odd threat from beyond human comprehension... No job is too big for AFTERLIFE INC.

But when the future looks this bright, it can be all too easy to neglect the past.

Ancient wheels are turning: remnants of the Empyrean's forgotten origins and its lost keepers. Terrible things are lurking beneath the surface of Jack's Brave New World...

And nothing stays buried forever.

*To Ben*
*Cheers!*

Afterlife Inc. created by Jon Lock

**LIFEBLOOD**
Written by Jon Lock
Pencils by Ash Jackson
Inks and colours by Nathan Ashworth
Colouring assistant: Taz Ashworth
Letters by Michael Stock

Published by Jon Lock Comics. "Afterlife Inc." and all characters, likenesses and situations featured herein are Copyright 2013 Jonathan Lock. All Rights Reserved. The characters, events and stories in this publication are entirely fictional. With the exception of art used for review purposes, none of the contents of this book may be reprinted in any form without the express written consent of the license holder.

First Edition. First Printing: November 2013

For more about Afterlife Inc. and Jon's other works visit www.jonlock.com

What did you think of this book? Please email any feedback to jonathanlock@btinternet.com. We look forward to hearing from you.

Connect with the world of Afterlife Inc.!
Follow on Facebook:  www.facebook.com/jonlockcomics
Twitter feed:  www.twitter.com/jonlockcomics

# CONTENTS

**When I die, I want to go to the Empyrean. I want to enter into the corporate family of Afterlife Inc. I want to entrust my death to Jack Fortune.**

I know I want all this because it's all so brilliantly and perfectly created and laid out in the pages of these books. Afterlife Inc. is a world ready for you to step right into. It's just a slight hurdle that you have to die before you can get in.

Afterlife Inc. is witty, original, unique and bold. It is witty with every silver-tipped word Jack Fortune says. It is original in its scope and setting, in the humanity of its unusual cast and the concept as a whole. It is unique in the way that I bet many people are repeatedly kicking their shins in the shins for not thinking of it first. And it's bold for tackling such big and ambitious ideas head on with huge page filling concepts that would make any other writer balk and turn back.

It makes me think of the feeling I had when I first opened books like Transmetropolitan and Planetary, or Invincible. Pure excitement. A feeling from the very beginning that you know this is going to be good and you can't wait to see where the writer takes you. The kind of feeling where you don't try and predict where the story's going to go, your brain just switches off and you're along for the ride. You just know you're in safe hands. These awesome characters in this startling world are going to hold your hand and run... and you're never going to be disappointed.

This is exactly what happens.

I crave the next volume of Afterlife Inc. as desperately as I crave the next volume of the big über-published graphic novels I collect from the big publishers because the standard of storytelling and balls-to-the-wall entertainment is just as high as in those books (if not higher).

Jon Lock is a gifted writer. Writing in comics is no easy task. Not only do you need to have that out-of-this-world idea that comics are so great for, that big concept that can't be told anywhere else... but you have to be able to express it page by page, panel by panel. Jon is an expert in this, knowing exactly how to space out his dialogue and when to introduce the next set-piece or pivotal scene as if by instinct. His quips and epic quotable one-liners fall into place on perfect page turns or at the very peak of a narrative climax and it sends shivers down your spine.

I am honoured to be able to call Jon a close friend, we are partners in the comics world and we have many collaborative projects planned for the future... but this book is ALL HIS. And I love that. Because no matter how teamed-up we get, how closely we work together... I can still look forward to the next volume of Afterlife Inc.

As I write this I haven't read this volume yet. I can't wait.

SPOILER ALERT: everyone's dead.

Nich Angell
*Salisbury 2013*

# ACKNOWLEDGEMENTS

This book exists thanks to the generosity of my Kickstarter backers. Because of these wonderful people, Afterlife Inc. has never felt more alive. I hope this story goes some way towards repaying my immense gratitude for their support.

Tom Sanders, Sophie Stanford-Tuck, Ben Tempest, Anthony O'Tierney, Caroline Hatchell, Aaron Macauley, Comfort Love and Adam Withers, Tony Johnson, Torn Saetern, Jonathan Tempest, Steve Farmer, Shane Chebsey of Scar Comics, Tomasz "Fanotherpg" Kaczmarek, Khiemble Trinhity, Mat Heagerty, Stefan Harkins, Josh Clarke, Michael Simkins, Ari Carr, Hannah Brown 1, Tom Huxley, Nancy Mitchell, Dan Hill, Rishdeep Thind, Keith Einmann, Jason Whaley, Hayley from KomiX in Melksham, Josh Alliston, Jen Smith, Andrew Jolley, Richard Hardy, Alison Waller, Hannah M, Thinkpadius, Sally Jane Thompson, Lawrence Harris, The Great Escape, Kash, Will Tempest, Dani Abram, Ali McLaren, PJ Montgomery, Jack Tempest, Ali White, Simon "Sim" Wellfair, Nikki Stu, Chris Ditchburn, Jack Devereaux, Sam Tempest, Leslie Kent, Aaron Smurf Murphy, Mark Wilko, Linda Ray, Travis Perkins, London Doby, Jr., Mháire Stritter, Andrew J Grant, Mike Garley, Matt Gibbs, Corey Brotherson, Michael Fabritius, Brian Rutledge, Mark Keating, Hannah Brown 2, Sean Smith, Steven Rutledge, Marie Mint, Millie Wokoma, Aydin Turgay, Scott Rhatigan, Mike Stock, Christopher Collins, Ayse Aksoy, John Steventon, Jack Davies, Ben Haith, Damon English, Bill Harris, Sonia Koval, Rory McGrath, Edmond Aggabao, Hywel Parrington, Thomas Krech, Simon M Poon, Chuck Suffel, Andy Bumpkin, Sam Beddoes, Joseph Gum, Paul Phelan, Adam Englebright, Zachary J. Vavrek, Nick Clarke, Laura Harris, Matt Ratcliffe, Wisewarrior Martial Arts, Roy Huteson Stewart, Will Train, Jess Waterman, Nathan Kai Wright, Steven D Quirke, Lizzie Boyle, Darren Ellis, Iain Holmes, Patrick J Walsh, Georgina Doji, Kevin Pass, Scott Jarratt, Ann Louise Gaunt, Catherine Smith, James Pegram, Graham Round, Pauline Widdows, Andrew Shirey, Nich Angell, Nick Baldwin, Eamon Knife, Luke Homer, Zach Suckle, Mayumi, Andy Bloor, Brett Johnson, James "Hiltz" Hilton, Chris Roberts, Gareth Evans, David Bishop, Stuart Gould, Mike Willis, Sam Roads, Jonty Levine, James "Snowy" Eastwood, Paddy Balch, G-Man from Comics Anonymous, Richard Holton, Walrus Face, Mark O'Donovan, Abigail Brady, Chris Ray, Amy and Mark Adams, Adam Poole, Jonathan Lancashire, Kevin Barber, Ben Fardon (Proud Lion), Carlos Anon, Nathan Adam Warner Davis, Jacob "Bellum" Davis, Kevin Young, Sean Gruosso, Ash M. Benson, Andy Agnew, Ash and Loosee Peters, Stefan Lew, Kevin Schantz, Tyler Van Hoevelaak, Andrew Stephens, Neil A Cook, Brandon Eaker, Robin Lock, Lucy Brown, Granddad, Nanna Sheila, Nain, Taid, Dad and Mam.

# LIFEBLOOD
## Chapter 1

# LIFEBLOOD
## Chapter 2

# LIFEBLOOD
## Chapter 3

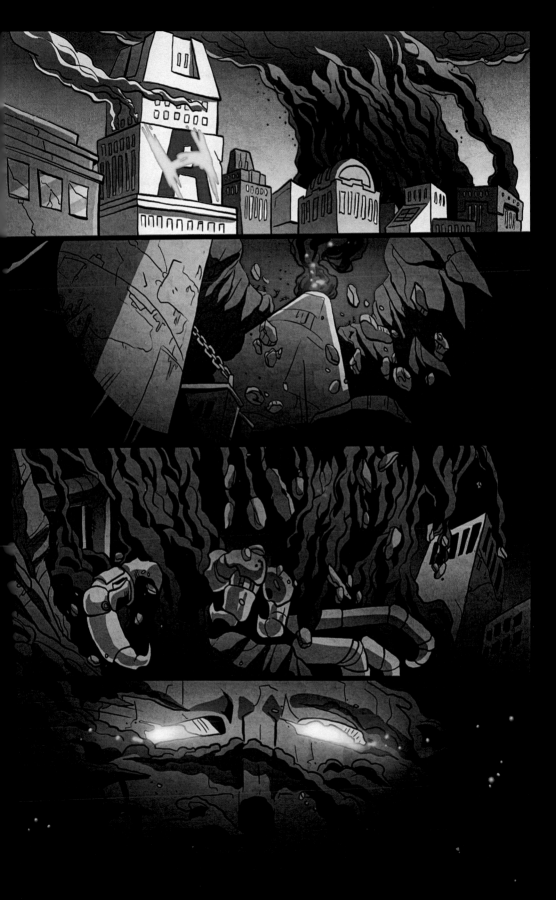

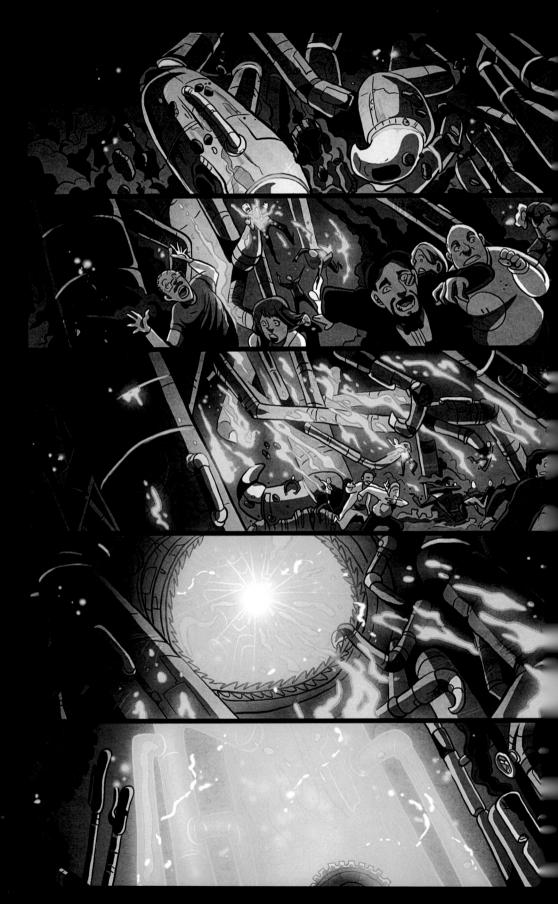

# LIFEBLOOD
## Chapter 4

FIN.

**This could have gone many ways. I know because I've tried. Ad nauseam, ad infinitum... Typing away with ravaged stumps in place of fingertips... So I'll heed some good advice and try for once in my life to keep things simple.**

I am, and forever will be, profoundly grateful for the support of my friends, family and fans while making AFTERLIFE INC. a reality. I wouldn't have got where I am today (wherever that may be) if it weren't for the wave of kindness buoying me up and pushing me forward. Because of you, what would otherwise have been the solitary ravings of a strange, hairy man have instead been committed to paper and inflicted upon an unsuspecting world. And may future generations judge you kindly...

To my Kickstarter backers, thank you for taking a chance on the little project that could, and allowing me to tell a story on the scale I've always dreamed of. This is the start of big things for Jack Fortune and colleagues... and it all started here with your trust and generosity.

To Ash, Nathan and Stocky... blessed with great patience and talent... whose pencils, inks, colours and letters have never been anything less than awe-inspiring... thank you for bringing my world to life so beautifully. It's been a pleasure to work alongside you for these 100 pages.

To Mam, Dad and Robin, thank you for more things than I could possibly list in the space of one page.

To Nich and Ali, thank you for the seemingly endless supply of laughter, Nerf, great taste and excellent company. And to Nich in particular, my thanks for an undeservedly glowing Foreword – we are talking about the same story, right?

To Lucy, thank you for making this all worthwhile. Playing around in the afterlife would be meaningless if life with you weren't so incredible.

And to all and sundry, let me leave you with some cryptic paraphrasing of the late, great Winston Churchill.

This is not the end.

This is not even the beginning of the end.

But it is, perhaps, the end of the beginning.

Boom.

Jon Lock
*Cheltenham 2013*

## SPECIAL FEATURES

# CAMEOS

In addition to the regular cast of AFTERLIFE INC. characters,
Lifeblood also plays host to some familiar faces...

During our time on Kickstarter, friend of
the book Adam went above and beyond the
call of duty in helping us reach our target.
To repay his efforts it seemed only fair to
feature him as Lux's inside man within
the ranks of the Undead.

And then brutally murder him...

Sadly, despite the best of intentions, the
screaming guitar solo didn't make the
final draft of the script. Apologies Adam.
Maybe next time. Or not...

Richard "Titch" Holton is one of my oldest friends and a constant source of inspiration, comedy and (frankly) baffling turns of phrase.

When it came to casting the latest addition to the AFTERLIFE INC. team, there was no one else I could imagine as Rich Fire. In fact, most of Fire's... *unique* dialogue has come directly from Titch at one point or another.

For some reason Titch was less than pleased with his previous incarnation in AFTERLIFE INC. as Doctor Holton from Near Life. Hopefully Rich Fire is something of a promotion.

Lifeblood also features the long overdue appearance of my girlfriend Lucy in an AFTERLIFE INC. book, seen here keeping a cool head during the Harvest's rampage (trademark hat also in shot).

AFTERLIFE·INC.

# PROFILE:
# ANGELS

The souls of the living must share the afterlife
with *others*. The angels. Soulless constructs built in
human – or less than human – form. Each has a specific
function within the grand engine of heaven. A role that
ensures the continued existence of the Empyrean.

Inspired by Afterlife Inc. many angels have now turned
their backs on their original programming to forge
lives of their own in this brave new afterlife. But not
everyone shares the joy of their liberation.

Forget wings, halos, cherubic smiles... these
are not the angels you were expecting.

And they were not made to be free.

*Art by Ash Jackson*

# LIFEBLOOD
## Epilogue

FIN.